MY
Magical
Bearded
FRIEND

WRITTEN BY
CHRIS HUSBAND

ILLUSTRATED BY
PATRICIA MOFFETT

To Jermaine And Ellie Rae
And of course Charlie the Cat
Chris Husband

My friend HAS A FINE CROP OF WHISKERS,
THAT *completely* ENVELOPE HIS

chin

THEY MAKE HIM LOOK JUST LIKE A BADGER,
WITH A PLEASANTLY WELCOMING GRIN

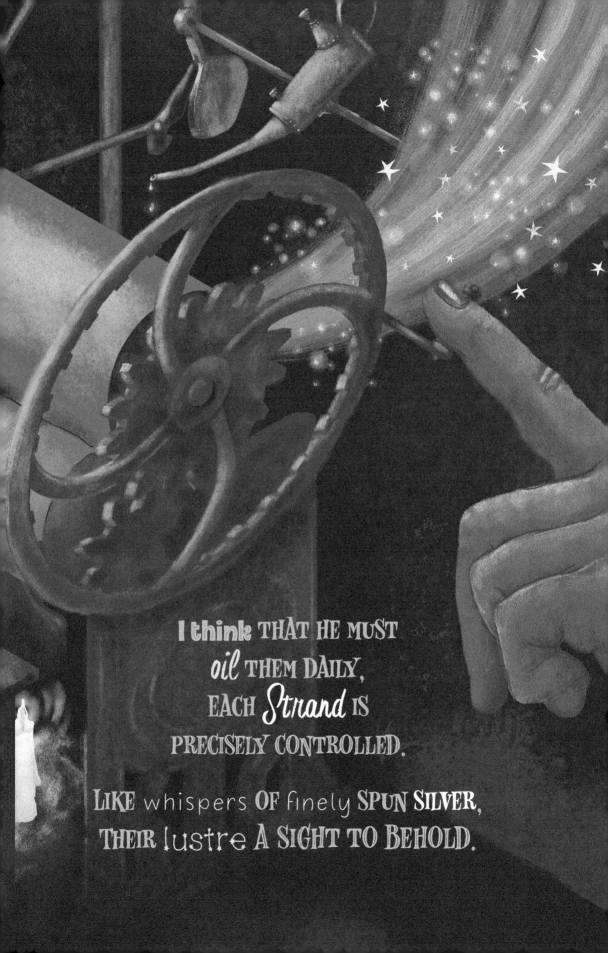

I think THAT HE MUST
oil THEM DAILY,
EACH *Strand* IS
PRECISELY CONTROLLED.

LIKE whispers OF finely SPUN SILVER,
THEIR lustre A SIGHT TO BEHOLD.

SUCH MAGNIFICENT FACIAL HAIR MAKES HIM
SO *Distinguished* AND REGAL TO SEE.

AN IMPORTANT OLD GENT ABOUT TOWN,
WHO surely HAS PLACES TO BE

HE CARRIES A cane
OF PURE WALNUT,

AND HIS HAT IS AS TALL AS A TREE.
EDGED WITH THE RICHEST OF SATIN,
AND A BROOCH MADE FROM gold FILIGREE.

HIS SUIT IS FROM *Saville Row* TAILORS,
NO SMARTER I'M SURE COULD BE FOUND.
HIS BOOTS ARE THE SOFTEST OF LEATHER,
WHOSE STEPS barely RAISE UP A SOUND.

THE SCENT OF COLOGNE IS EXQUISITE
AND PUTS DREAMERS INTO A TRANCE

A TIE PIN OF OPALS AND DIAMONDS
JUST ADDS TO HIS AIR OF ROMANCE

SO IF YOUR PATHS CROSS ACCIDENTALLY,
AND YOU HAPPEN TO CAPTURE HIS GAZE,

TOUCH THE PEAK OF YOUR CAP
AND BOW GRANDLY
AND UTTER THIS
respectful PHRASE ...

"Good Day Sir,
I trust you are well,
Sir?"

THEN LISTEN AS HE PASSES BY ...

WITH HIS QUIET, MELODIOUS TIMBRE
YOU MAY JUST THEN CATCH HIS REPLY.

"*A Good Day to you too*
dearest friend.
Fine weather
we'll be having today"

THEN WITH A THEATRICAL
WAVE OF HIS HAND
HE WILL
silently
HURRY AWAY.

IF YOU TURN FOR JUST

ONE.

MORE.

LOOK.

AT HIS MARVELLOUS, LUSTROUS

BEARD

YOU MAY FIND THAT MY FRIEND IS

NO LONGER IN SIGHT

HE HAS

magically

disappeared!

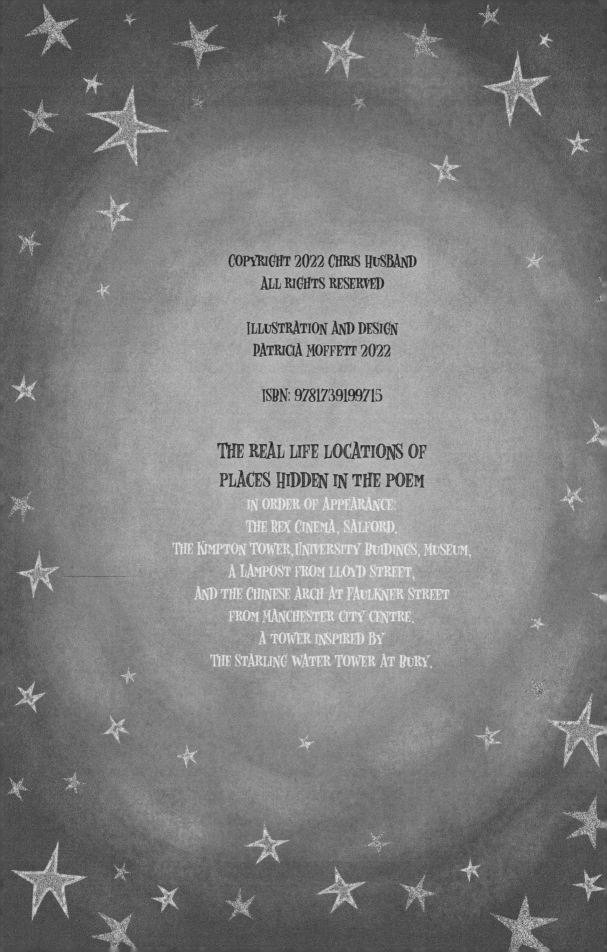

ISBN: 9781739199715

The real life locations of
places hidden in the poem
in order of appearance:
The Rex Cinema, Salford.
The Kimpton Tower, University Buidings, Museum,
A Lampost from Lloyd Street,
And the Chinese Arch at Faulkner Street
from Manchester City Centre.
A tower inspired by
The Starling Water Tower at Bury.

Lightning Source UK Ltd.
Milton Keynes UK
UKHW051310251122
412651UK00012B/172